National
Museums
Scotland

Greyfriars Bobby
A Tale of Victorian Edinburgh

Frances and Gordon Jarvie

SCOTTIES SERIES EDITORS
Frances and Gordon Jarvie

D0313793

Contents

Bobby's century 2
What's in a story? 4
Swanston 6
Mr Traill's Dining-Rooms 8
Cowgate lodgings 10
Greyfriars Kirkyard 12
Back to Swanston Farm 14
Working his keep 16
On the loose 18
The long arm of the law 20
Meeting the Lord Provost 22

A soldier's world 24
Feted at the Castle 26
Celebrity status 28
William Chambers 30
Angela Burdett-Coutts 32
William Brodie 33
Edinburgh's epidemics 34
Bobby's Edinburgh 36
Bobby's breed: why the name? 38
Answers/Useful websites 40
Facts and activities section . . . . i-viii

Published in 2010 by
NMS Enterprises Limited – Publishing
a division of NMS Enterprises Limited
National Museums Scotland
Chambers Street, Edinburgh EH1 1JF

Text © Frances and Gordon Jarvie 2010

Images (for © information see below and page
viii of the Facts and activities section)

ISBN: 978-1-905267-41-5

British Library Cataloguing in Publication Data
A catalogue record of this book
is available from the British Library.

Book design concept by Redpath.
Cover design by Mark Blackadder.
Layout by NMSE – Publishing.
Printed and bound in the United Kingdom by
Bell & Bain Ltd, Glasgow.

CREDITS

*Thanks are due to all individuals and organisations
who supplied images and photographs for this
publication. Every attempt has been made to contact copyright holders to use the material contained
within. If any image has been inadvertently missed,
please contact the publisher.*

COVER ILLUSTRATIONS
Greyfriars Kirk from *Daniel Wilson: Memorials of
Edinburgh in the Olden Time* – (Hugh Paton:
Edinburgh, 1843); Greyfriars Bobby statue
(National Museums Scotland).

NATIONAL MUSEUMS SCOTLAND
(© National Museums Scotland) – for pages 2 (Irish
potato famine); 3 (Bell's telephone reproduction,
Forth Rail Bridge opening [from *Illustrated London
News*] & Tay Bridge disaster [*ILN*]); 4 (emigrants
[*ILN*]); 5 (Traill family with Bobby); 6 (shepherd &
Pentland Hills); 8 (Mr Traill); 9 (surgeon's tools);
12 (mort-collar); 15 (corn harvesters & Swanston

Farm steading), 16 (a Newhaven fishwife); 17
(calotype camera & masons); 22 (Bobby's collar);
24 (Firing a ceremonial gun [D. O. Hill and R.
Adamson, 1843-49]); 26 (Victoria Cross & 42nd
Highlanders); 27 ('The Thin Red Line', by Robert
Gibb, 1881); 28 (water pump & Greyfriars Bobby
statue); 30 (Chambers statue); 31 (Chambers
Street & Museum of Science and Art); 34 (Old
Royal Infirmary); 37 (Heriot's School); 39 (James
Hogg statue); Facts and activities section, page i
(Greyfriars Bobby statue); v (Nipper on record).

FURTHER CREDITS (see page viii of Facts and
activities section)

SCOTTIE BOOKS

For a full listing of NMS Enterprises Limited –
Publishing titles and related merchandise:
www.nms.ac.uk/books

Bobby's century

IRISH POTATO FAMINE

Greyfriars Bobby was born around 1856 or 57. He died in Edinburgh in January 1872. Find out about some of the other events that occurred during his lifetime and during his century.

- **1801** – Thomas Jefferson is elected President of the United States.
- The Kingdoms of Great Britain and Ireland join to form the United Kingdom.
- Napoleon Bonaparte crowns himself Emperor of France.
- **1804** – Richard Trevithick designs the first realistic steam locomotive.
- **1805** – Britain wins the Battle of Trafalgar against the French and Spanish naval fleets.
- **1806** – The Holy Roman Empire is dissolved after the Treaty of Pressburg.
- **1807** – Britain declares the Slave Trade illegal.

THE GREAT EXHIBITION

- **1812** – France invades Russia during Napoleonic Wars.
- **1812-15** – War between the United States and United Kingdom.
- **1814** – George Stephenson designs the 'Rocket' loco-motive.
- **1815** – Congress of Vienna (Europe undergoes great changes).
- Napoleon is defeated at the Battle of Waterloo by Britain.
- **1816** – Shaka takes over the Zulu kingdom.
- Freezing temperatures in the Northern hemisphere.
- **1819** – Honours of Scotland (Crown Jewels) are put on display at Edinburgh Castle.
- James Watt, Scottish inventor and engineer, dies.
- **1820** – George IV becomes King of the United Kingdom.
- **1821-27** – Greek War of Independence.
- **1823** – The British Empire annexes Burma.
  - **1829** – Resurrection-man William Burke is hanged in Edinburgh for the murder of innocent people for anatomical supply. His partner-in-crime William Hare turns King's Evidence and is granted his freedom.

- **1830** – William IV ascends the throne of the United Kingdom.
- Revolution in France (July).
- Belgium is created.
- **1832** – Reform Act gives the vote to more people.
- Anatomy Act introduced after Burke and Hare murder case.
- Death of Sir Walter Scott.
- **1833** – Slavery Abolition Act bans slavery throughout the British Empire.
- **1837** Queen Victoria's reign begins.
- **1840** – New Zealand is founded as a nation.
- **1844** – Samuel Morse sends the world's first telegraph line message between Baltimore and Washington.
- **1845-59** – The Irish Potato Famine leads to mass emigrations.
- **1847** – Scottish doctor James Young Simpson demonstrates the effects of chloroform.
- **1848** – California Gold Rush.
- Queen Victoria leases Balmoral estate on Deeside.
- **1850** – 'The Little Ice Age' of bitterly cold weather comes to an end.

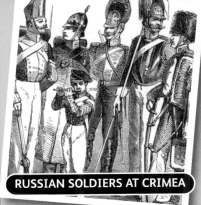

RUSSIAN SOLDIERS AT CRIMEA

- **1851** – The Great Exhibition in London. The United Kingdom is the first country in the world to industrialise.
- **1853-56** – Crimean War between France, United Kingdom, Ottoman Empire against Russia.
- **1856** – Death of Scottish geologist and religious writer, Hugh Miller.
- **1857-58** – Indian Rebellion.
- **1859** – Charles Darwin's influential *Origin of the Species* is published.
- **1861-65** – American Civil War between the Union and the Confederacy.
- **1861** – First firing of the One o'Clock Gun at Edinburgh Castle.
- **1863** – The International Red Cross is created; First Geneva Convention (1864).
- **1865-77** – United States constitution is changed; slavery is banned.
- **1865** – End of American Civil War; but President Abraham Lincoln is assassinated.
- **1866** – First Transatlantic telegraph cable successfully sent.
- **1867** – First football club founded in Scotland (Queen's Park).
- Suez Canal opens between the Mediterranean and Red Sea.
- **1870-71** – Franco-Prussian War.

- **1871-1914** – Second phase of the Industrial Revolution.
- **1872** – First international football game – Scotland versus England.
- **1873** – Death of Scottish explorer David Livingstone.
- **1874** – First public art exhibition by the Impressionists.
- **1874-75** – Spain becomes a Republic.
- **1875-1900** – Famine in India.
- **1876** – Alexander Graham Bell files patent for his telephone.

BELL'S TELEPHONE

- **1878** – Tay Bridge opens.
- **1879** – Tay Bridge collapses with tragic consequences.
- Death of scientist James Clerk Maxwell.
- **1882** – British invasion and occupation of Egypt.

- **1883** – Krakatoa volcano explodes!
- **1885** – Scottish Office created.
- Robert Louis Stevenson publishes *The Strange Case of Dr Jekyll and Mr Hyde*.
- **1887** – New Tay Bridge opens.
- **1888** – Jack the Ripper's reign of terror in London.
- **1890** – Prince of Wales opens Forth Rail Bridge.
- Last battle in the American Indian Wars at Wounded Knee.
- **1894** – Death of Scottish writer Robert Louis Stevenson.
- **1896** – Olympic Games begin again in Athens.
- **1899** – Second Boer War.

FORTH RAIL BRIDGE OPENING

TAY BRIDGE DISASTER

What's in a story?

Animal stories are much loved, because they often mirror human behaviour in simple ways. Special favourites are stories about dogs.

Thanks to an Edinburgh dog-lover – William Chambers, Lord Provost of Edinburgh from 1865 to 1869 – the licence fee was paid for a homeless Skye terrier called Greyfriars Bobby. The dog was presented with a collar inscribed 'Greyfriars Bobby from the Lord Provost, 1867' and he received the freedom of the city. The collar is now displayed, along with his bowl, in the Museum of Edinburgh in the Canongate. From these bald facts an enduring legend began.

The legend inspired American author and journalist Eleanor Stackhouse Atkinson to find out more about the famous dog. Her novel *Greyfriars Bobby* became her most famous book and has been in print continuously since its publication in 1912. Atkinson may well have visited Edinburgh to research the background for her book.

Eleanor Stackhouse Atkinson

Eleanor Atkinson (1863-1942) was American-born and lived far from Edinburgh. She grew up in the Cornbelt state of Indiana, on the great plains of the American Midwest. Her early memories were of her mother reading poetry to her by Robert Burns, Walter Scott and Alfred Lord Tennyson.

She may also have read another Scottish story about a faithful dog, *Rab and His Friends* (1859), by the Edinburgh surgeon Dr John Brown (1810-82). This and Brown's other dog stories appealed to Victorian tastes and all his books were widely read. The stories of Rab and of Greyfriars Bobby probably reached Atkinson via Scottish emigrant neighbours in the Midwest;

Emigration ships (right), took thousands of Scots to the New World. Although some found their destinations and climate harsh and inhospitable, others prospered from freedom and opportunity.

Scots emigration to the United States was at its peak during the second half of the 19th century. The emigrants' accents were unchanged, and they continued until the second generation to speak the Scots heard back home.

A letter in *The Scotsman* in 1953 offered one confirmation of Bobby's story among many. William Dow, a joiner and cabinetmaker at George Heriot's Hospital, a charitable school, had often used the path leading through the Greyfriars Kirkyard to a coffee-house. His daughter remembered his stories of a little dog running to her father and following him along to Mr Traill's Dining-Rooms, where Bobby was given a meal. The period was dated to around 1858, when our story begins ....

Legends tend to be made up from a mix of invention plus historical facts, such as the stories of King Robert the Bruce and the spider, Robin Hood and his merry men, King Arthur and his Knights of the Round Table. Greyfriars Bobby is another such story. We know the facts of his meetings with the Lord Provost and the famous inscribed collar presented to him in 1867; we know of his meetings with Angela Burdett-Coutts who paid for the statue of Bobby, and with the sculptor William Brodie who created it; we also know the facts that surround his death. But we are less sure about Bobby's early days. We can only say that Eleanor Atkinson's 1912 story creates a *likely* scenario; the authors of this book have been content to follow it almost a hundred years later.

What is a legend?

Mr John Traill, owner of the Dining-Rooms frequented by Auld Jock and Bobby, and his daughter and son, with Greyfriars Bobby on the lap of Mrs Traill.

Swanston

The story begins in 1858. A shepherd, John Gray, known as Auld Jock, stands on Caerketton Hill, taking in the view as far as the eye can see ....

Auld Jock the shepherd looked around his world from the high crest of Caerketton Hill. He looked south to the misty hills around Peebles, west along the ridge to Allermuir Hill, north to the spires, roofs and turrets of Edinburgh and beyond to the Firth of Forth and to Fife. It was a crisp November morning and Jock was well happed up in his heavy greatcoat and shepherd's plaid, but he was shivering.

This shepherd from Perthshire, c.1900, is wearing his plaid in the traditional manner that Auld Jock might have adopted. It served two main purposes: to keep him warm on the hills and to cradle lambs or other vulnerable creatures.

A shepherd rounds up his sheep against the impressive backdrop of the Pentland Hills and Swanston steading in 1949. Little had changed since Auld Jock's time, except for the electric pylons of course! Caerketton's summit is on the right.

From the slopes below him he spotted a sudden flurry of long hair louping towards him. Bobby, the young Skye terrier, rushed up to Auld Jock and tugged at him. He knew it was market day in the city! The pair were soon back at Swanston Farm, where the farmer had his cart ready for their journey to Edinburgh's Grassmarket.

Swanston tales

Swanston's name came from the Norse words for **Sveinn's Farm**. Today it is one of Edinburgh's most picturesque villages and a conservation area. Look for the T-wood (in the middle of the picture) on the slopes of Caerketton: it is actually in the shape of a cross when seen from the air.

For Bobby, ears twitching with excitement, the Grassmarket was heiven, with the thrang of horses, cattle and sheep, the smells and noisy crowds beneath the Castle Rock. Then an ear-splitting bang announced the One o'Clock Gun from the Castle – when Bobby raced to Auld Jock's usual haunt in the near-by coffee-house. Skeltering over the cobbled streets, slithering to a halt at Auld Jock's inglenook, Bobby found a gallus soldier in his master's place! But where was Auld Jock?

Bobby hurtled back outside, through Greyfriars Kirkyard, and down into the dingy Cowgate. There, on an old, rickety carrier's cart, lay a fevered Jock. 'I'm jist a muckle sumph the day!' said the old man. Bobby smelt trouble, and snuggled into the crook of his master's arm.

Scots corner

gallus	smart
happed	wrapped
heivin	heaven
inglenook	fireplace; fire burning on a hearth
louping	leaping
muckle sumph	big dafty
thrang	bustle, throng

Website watch

Take a look at:
www.ordnancesurvey.co.uk/oswebsite/opendata/viewer/

Type in the postcode **EH10 7DT** on the Get-a-map by Ordnance Survey and zoom in on **Swanston**. Then find the burn running through the village. Look out for **Caerketton** and **Allermuir Hill**, and for **Windy Door Nick** between the two hills. Do you know what **Windy Door Nick** is?

Answer on page 40

To Edinburgh ...

The view of Edinburgh from Craiglockhart, a village on the way into the city from Swanston. This painting, thought to be by the Rev. John Thomson 'of Duddingston' (1778-1840), shows Edinburgh to be a small city by the standards of today. Thomson was an amateur painter, but kept company with artists Sir Henry Raeburn and J. M. W. Turner, and was a great friend of the author Sir Walter Scott.

Mr Traill's Dining-Rooms

Bobby came from a long line of feisty Skye terriers. Ready to obey but with a stubborn streak, he sensed Auld Jock was now badly in need of his company.

Scots corner

copper	penny
hertsome	encouraging
ma ain	my own
stramash	commotion

Jock's work for the season was over. He'd led a hard and often lonely life tending flocks of Cheviot and Blackface sheep. But he knew that Bobby would have to be returned to the farm at Swanston. As icy rain fell, the lamplighter tended his gas lamps and Jock struggled up Candlemaker Row towards Mr Traill and his Dining-Rooms. He'd dozed fitfully for hours.

A hertsome Bobby led Jock towards food and warmth. Mr Traill helped Jock out of his dripping plaid and teased him for being so canny about the awful weather. 'Ay, it's misty – mebbe makin for snaw,' he'd said. As Jock slowly thawed out at the crackling coal fire, Bobby shook himself dry, and with nose twitching, scampered about the familiar room. Mr Traill quietly looked again at the now slowly snoring Jock. 'Hot mutton broth wi' porridge in it is what you're wanting. And tae see a doctor …'.

Startled, Jock woke up. There was no way he was going near a place for the sick and destitute. Rummaging in a pocket he put down a copper for a plate of broth for Bobby and explained, 'He isna ma ain dug'. Mr Traill suggested Jock could make a pouch in his plaid to hide Bobby for the night when he went to his lodgings. He dropped some scotch buns into Auld Jock's greatcoat for Bobby. The warmth and food soon made Jock nod off again – this time with a rattling sound in his chest. Alarmed, Mr Traill rushed out into the murk to find a doctor. After entreating help, he quickly returned – but Auld Jock and Bobby had vanished.

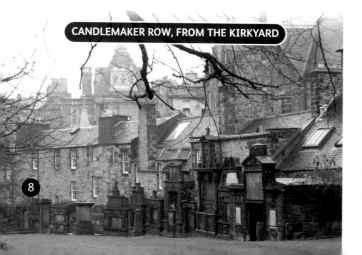

CANDLEMAKER ROW, FROM THE KIRKYARD

Victorian Edinburgh

The first Royal Infirmary (left) was a four-storey building facing across Infirmary Street. There was a large operating theatre, with tiered seating, where students could watch the surgeons at work. In the pre-anaesthetic days it must have been gruesome!

Tools of the surgeon's trade, dated to the first half of the 19th century.

The Grassmarket lies below the steep Castle Rock. It was where beasts were bought and sold, as well as being a marketplace for hay, corn and seed. Huge crowds used to relish watching the executions that took place there. On market days it was full of drovers, dealers, pedlars, pickpockets, acrobats and street players – all creating a stramash!

Cowgate lodgings

Jock and Bobby now faced a short but treacherous walk as they slithered over the icy cobbles and down into the dark gorge of the Cowgate.

Edinburgh tenements in the mid-19th century were known for their squalid conditions. There were no toilets or pipes to take human waste away. Instead, it was tossed out of the window into the gutters below, with a shout of 'gardy-loo' to warn any passers-by. This meant 'watch out for the slops!'

Tall tenements were tumbled together in wynds and closes. They had been abandoned long since by the better-off who had moved to the airy spaces of the New Town. With the frosty air in his lungs, Jock peched up to a seventh landing. He clung on to the banister and started a coughing fit. Still, he remembered to hide Bobby in his plaid before facing the old crone of a landlady, who grasped his coins, biting them between her teeth to test them!

Smothering his cough, Auld Jock reached the attic stairs to the very top of the tenement where there were tiny rooms divided by flimsy partitions. 'Have a care, Bobby,' Jock warned, opening his window and bringing in a pot of heather from the stone ledge. The mere smell of it transported him back to his beloved hills and Bobby yelped with excitement. A stushie from his neighbours soon passed and Jock, wabbit from this escapade, collapsed on to his bed.

Jock didn't stir until mid-day, with an anxious Bobby licking his outstretched hand. The old shepherd awoke to see the snow-clad Pentland Hills far to the south, but staggered back to bed in a heap. Feeding Bobby one of the buns he'd found, he slowly counted out his savings and reckoned he could avoid the Infirmary.

From the bed Jock wheezed at Bobby, 'Awa' hame, laddie, awa' hame'. Bobby patiently guarded his master for two days before worn-out Jock finally died of pneumonia. A policeman, seeing the coins under the pillow, arranged a funeral at the nearby Greyfriars Kirk. The humble cortège was followed by a loyal Bobby who flattened himself on the new grave. 'Awa' oot,' cried the sexton James Brown, gently lifting him over the gate. But thrawn Bobby had other ideas – James Brown was going to see a lot more of this wee dog.

The Cowgate (*gate* = walk) was known as the 'Irish Quarter' after thousands of Irish people flocked here after the Great Famine of 1846. It was once a country lane for leading cows to pasture land beyond the city walls. For Auld Jock it was a disease-ridden slum with crumbling tenements, filthy closes and no sanitation or running water.

Scots corner

canny	careful
peched	struggled, panted
sexton	caretaker
stushie	racket
thrawn	determined
wabbit	weak, exhausted

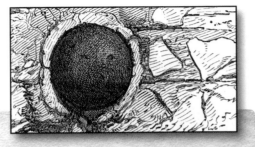

Cannonball House

On the west wall of Cannonball House (at the foot of the Castle Esplanade) you can see a cannonball embedded in the wall. It was placed there to mark the height of 329 feet above sea level, in comparison to the higher point at Comiston springs. It confirmed that water was supplied to the city by gravity feed.

Water for sale

We take our clean water supply for granted – unless there's a problem like a burst water main or a drought. For Auld Jock there was no such luxury. In his day, water was drawn from wells and pumps. Spring water from Comiston and Swanston was fed by gravity to a great storage tank at Castlehill. Water was only turned on at certain times, with long queues forming, waiting with pitchers and casks.

Queue-jumpers were given a hefty fine! The lucky ones hired water caddies (a carrier or porter), such as the man on the right, who got priority and sold water at a regulated price. Visit the Museum of Edinburgh at Huntly House in the Canongate to see the original water pipes from 1761. What are they made from?

Answer on page 40

Greyfriars Kirkyard

Mystery object

Do you know what this object is?
A clue – it was used in graveyards.

Answer on page 40

Just after the boom of the One o'Clock Gun had died away, Bobby came nuzzling at Mr Traill's trouser leg.

Five days had passed since the death of Auld Jock and the wee dog was looking frail. As Mr Traill laid him down under the settle, he could clearly feel the dog's bones. Bobby received the finest plate of broth, followed by warm haggis. After this delicious feast he fell into a welcome snooze. When this was interrupted by the sunset bugle call from the Castle, a livelier Bobby wagged his tail in thanks and trotted off.

The imposing façade of Greyfriars Kirk nestles among the gables and chimneys of Candlemaker Row. In the background you can just see Heriot's charitable school (see page 19).

Puzzled, Mr Traill followed him down the street to the Kirkyard gate. Bobby was trying frantically to unlatch it. 'What are ye prowling about here for?' came a booming voice from the gloaming. It was the care-taker of the graveyard, James Brown. Bobby disappeared at once.

Darkness was falling as the men searched behind the slabs, under the table-tombs, and around the Martyrs' Monument. They asked at the tenement windows that faced the Kirk-yard wall. One lassie had spied Bobby peeping up at her. Mr Traill offered a shilling to her, or to any bairn, that could find the dog for him. Then the two men sat on a slab and blethered about this dog that had such a mind of its own.

As if hearing their conversation, Bobby stepped back into view. Mr Traill lifted him up gently, but the wee dog wriggled back down. Thrawn Bobby had them both bumbazed, and James Brown was certainly not going to break the 'NO DOGS ALLOWED' bye-law. Bobby was banished to the street again. But by eight o'clock a constant howling at the gate forced Mr Traill to persuade Geordie, a local lad, to smuggle Bobby back into the Kirkyard. Bobby was where he belonged once again – at his master's grave. He slept soundly that night.

THE MARTYRS' MONUMENT

- What is a martyr?
- Who were the Covenanters? (Try looking up the Battle of Bothwell Bridge or Rullion Green.)
- What happened to the Covenanters' leaders?
- Where were most of the martyrs buried?

Answers on page 40

Left: The Martyrs' Monument in Greyfriars Kirkyard.

Right: A painting of 'Greyfriars Bobby' by John McLeod.

Scots corner

blethered	chatted
bumbazed	bewildered
gloaming	dusk
kirk, kirkyard	church, churchyard

Greyfriars Kirk

1562 Once a monastery garden of the Franciscan or Grey Friars, Mary, Queen of Scots granted the abandoned garden to the Town Council for use as a burial ground.

1620 Greyfriars was the first new kirk or church built in Edinburgh after the Reformation.

1638 The Greyfriars congregation signed the National Covenant here on 28th February, along with the city's noblemen and merchants. They pledged to fight for their religion, free from the influence of Rome and the interference of King Charles I.

1650 The interior of the church was wrecked by Oliver Cromwell's soldiers, who used it as a barracks.

1706 The Martyrs' Monument was built at the side of the graveyard backing onto Candlemaker Row, in memory of executed Covenanters.

1718 Gunpowder stored by the Town Council in the church tower exploded, and the steeple blew up.

1845 The church was restored after a serious fire.

Back to Swanston Farm

ROBERT BURNS

The world-famous Scottish poet, Robert Burns, was reputedly the source of Greyfriars Bobby's name.

Word was left at all the inns around the markets for the farmer from Swanston to come and reclaim Bobby.

Later that week, a burly figure with a huge Clydesdale horse confronted Mr Traill. 'Is Bobby with ye? My wee lass is pining for him.'

Mr Traill was still puzzled about Auld Jock's abandonment of Bobby, but slowly the sad story was unravelled. Bobby approached, his sharp ears twitching at the name of his dear master – and was promptly bundled into a lidded basket. To delay their return to Swanston, Mr Traill asked about the name Bobby.

'Oh, it was a leddy who called him that, after Bobby Burns the poet,' said the farmer.

Bobby's howling subsided into whimpers on the long plod back from Lauriston to Boroughmuir, and up by Fairmilehead towards Swanston. All the way he sniffed at the various town and country smells wafting through his basket. On arrival, the farmer's lass rushed out to the yard – 'Can I haud him now, faither?' But not until the door was firmly snecked did they release Bobby. They were taking no chances this time! Among the sheepdogs at the busy hearth, Bobby allowed himself to be petted while Auld Jock's plight was explained to the farmer's wife.

Swanston tales

Part of the old lands of Swanston were called **Temple Lands**. Knights of the Temple protected pilgrims on visits to the Holy Lands. (The badge of the Knights Templar was the **Maltese Cross**.) Perhaps Swanston had been a stopping place for the Templars on those long journeys.

In the 17th century, Swanston Farm was a refuge for the Covenanters, who often held their meetings in the Pentland Hills. Food and drink was always available for those who chapped at the farmhouse door – the kitchen dresser was laid out with bread, cheese, bannocks, milk and brandy.

As the family blethered, Bobby was creeping back to the door, scratching it, and begging to be allowed out. Finally the farmer's strong arm gripped the wee dog and took him out to the barn, where his lass tried to bed him down for the night. She shut the door, calling out 'Goodnight'.

No time to lose – Bobby explored his new quarters, soon scraping, digging and squeezing his way under the door. Then he was running back down towards the city, over fields, through burns, across gardens, until he reached Lauriston Place at last. Here he heard the bugle call from the Castle, and dashed toward the Kirkyard gate. He was just in time to avoid James Brown, the sexton. Bobby scurried under the table-top tomb – home at last for another good night's sleep beside his master's grave.

Author Robert Louis Stevenson used the Covenanter setting of Swanston Farm (in the background) in his novel *St Ives*. A French officer in the Napoleonic wars, newly escaped from Edinburgh Castle, was hidden in nearby Swanston Cottage. The young 'RLS' later spent several summers there. The Pentland Hills have been described as 'the birthplace of the genius of RLS'.

Farming festivals

The highlight of the farming year at Swanston was the **kirn** or **hairst** – a ceilidh-type celebration to mark the end of the harvest, held in the barn of Swanston Farm.

Squads of reapers worked northwards from Berwickshire through Lothian and north to Fife. A corn dolly was made from the last sheaf of corn, and hung up until New Year, when it was either burned or ploughed back into the land.

New Year was the only other holiday that Auld Jock would have enjoyed. Our New Year's Day festival replaced **Auld Handsel Monday**, a January festival especially for domestic servants and farmworkers, who enjoyed very few leisure days. (A **handsel** was a gift or a gratuity.)

Harvesting corn in the Lothians in the late 1800s.

ROBERT LOUIS STEVENSON

Working his keep

On the right is 'Phemie', a fishwife. She has travelled by tram all the way to Corstorphine village from Newhaven, with her willow basket, creel and gutting board, to sell fish newly caught that day. Her traditional clothes would not have changed much since Bobby's day.

Late dawn, a winter morning, a thin powder of dry snow …

Bobby woke to calls of 'Caller herrin!' from the Newhaven fishwives, and 'Are ye cauld?' from men selling firewood. He had to work out his own survival plan, and get James Brown and Mr Traill onside. As a huge rat darted past his nose, Bobby snapped at it, killing it with one bite. Problem solved – Bobby's natural talent would impress the caretaker. The wee dog would clear the Kirk-yard of vermin, and lay the bodies out for inspection on Auld Jock's grave.

As the city stirred and smoke curled upwards from the forest of chimney-pots, Bobby greeted Mr Brown with upturned nose and dark appealing eyes. 'Good gracious!' the sexton exclaimed, as he took in the scene. 'Jeanie – see what the dog's done noo!'

Having fully convinced the Browns of his worth, Bobby trotted off home with them, submitting to a bath and – much more important – a meal. He even tholed being groomed, despite his tangled coat.

Back in the graveyard, Bobby was always on the alert for the rattle of the gate being opened. From a tiny upstairs window in Candlemaker Row, he was spotted by local bairns, Tam and Ailie. Between them, they

Cries of Old Edinburgh

- 'Caller herrin', whae will buy?' was the famous cry from the Newhaven fishwives (see photograph above).

- 'Razors, knives and shears to grind, / I'm sure I'll sharp them tae yer mind,' called the knife-grinder.

- 'Caller osts' (oysters), old clothes, pies, bird-seed – all manner of things were sold in the streets and closes of the Old Town. By 1851 there were still 40,000 people living in the crowded Old Town, but many of the better off folk now lived in the spacious New Town.

Revolution behind the lens!

David Octavius Hill and Robert Adamson were probably the all-time best early photographic partnership. They took some of the finest photos – over 3000 in a three-year period around Edinburgh in the 1840s. They left a magnificent record of the ordinary folk going about their business in the capital – one of the best early examples of photo journalism.

Scots corner

caller	fresh, cold
dumfoonert	dumbfounded, amazed
snecked	bolted, locked
tholed	tolerated

lifted the wee dog and triumphantly carried him over to Mr Traill's. The dumfoonert landlord soon rewarded his young guests – and Bobby – with a fine feed. The landlord hoped the dog might stay, but as soon as Bobby had been fed he shot out the door to return to his duties. Then it was Mr Brown's turn to try and keep him indoors overnight. But Bobby's need was clear and constant – he had to be with Auld Jock.

Left: This early calotype camera with lens, c.1840, was used by Fox Talbot, the inventor of the photographic negative/positive process. This is the type of camera Hill and Adamson would have used.

Below: An example of a Hill and Adamson calotype image that shows masons working on the Scott Monument in 1844 (see page 33).

17

On the loose

Discovery trail

Look at the George Heriot's School emblem and its motto below. Does your town, city or school have a motto? Is there a story behind it?

The month of May in the grave-yard brought out flowers – and the weeds – in abundance.

James Brown toiled long hours to keep it all tidy, while Bobby swiftly despatched any skulking cats looking for fledglings. He still avoided strangers in case they forced him to return to Swanston, and he would instantly disappear at the click of the Kirk-yard gate. The only people who knew about Bobby's new home were Mr Brown and Jeanie his wife, Mr Traill, some of the neighbours in Candlemaker Row, and, of course, a few of the boys from Heriot's.

A pleasant routine of a mid-day meal at Mr Traill's, a runabout in the neighbourhood, and supper at the kitchen door of the Browns' lodge, was Bobby's perfect day. It was only bettered if some of the tenement or Heriot's children came out to play.

A photograph of Greyfriars Bobby, dated c.1865, by an unknown artist.

18

Geordie Ross and Sandy McGregor often leapt over the Heriot's wall on a Saturday. Geordie would pretend to fill a pipe, and say, 'I'm Jinglin Geordie Heriot – a prood goldsmith fit to smoke wi' a king'. Sandy would then whistle like a mavis to attract Bobby. What adventures they had with the wee dog! Bobby had slithered over ice at Duddingston Loch in winter; he'd tramped over the Boroughmuir trying not to annoy the golfers; he'd even been as far as Leith to sniff the sea. A group of Geordie's friends once took Bobby up onto the Castle Rock, where they pretended to be the Light Brigade at Balaclava. 'Up and at them!' yelled Sandy as they all tumbled down the slopes, with Bobby barking his delight.

Scots corner

jinglin	jingling
leal	loyal
mavis	song-thrush
prood	proud

James Brown was still troubled. Would the Minister of Greyfriars find out about Bobby? Would the sexton lose his job? The Minister knew better. He had long since heard of Bobby, and of the lonely death of Auld Jock. He knew an answer was needed to Bobby's ownership. 'Everyone's dog is no one's dog. I'll speak to my elders about it – in due course,' he said, patting the wee dog's head. Bobby had heard every word.

Mystery object

Can you guess what this unusual object is? And what do you think it might be made of?

Answers on page 40

Jinglin Geordie

George Heriot (1563-1624) (above), nicknamed 'Jinglin Geordie' by Sir Walter Scott in one of his novels, was a goldsmith. He became rich through his role as a money-lender to King James VI of Scotland (I of England), after being appointed jeweller and goldsmith to the King in 1601. In 1603, after the Union of the Crowns, Heriot followed the King to London.

Having had two sons who died, Heriot left a very large sum of money to found a 'hospital' for 'puir faitherless bairns' in his home city of Edinburgh. Built in the 1630s shortly after Greyfriars Kirk, this became George Heriot's School. One of the first monuments erected in Greyfriars Kirkyard was to Heriot, and there is a gate from the school into the Kirkyard.

The long arm of the law

For many years after Auld Jock's death, Bobby was as smart and cantie as ever, his hazel-brown eyes still twinkling. But Mr Traill had begun to notice that Bobby's after-dinner naps were getting longer.

A cocky sergeant from the Castle was a guest at the Dining-Rooms one afternoon, and he offered to buy Bobby – much to Mr Traill's annoyance. The sergeant had provoked him and he was told in no uncertain terms that Bobby wasn't for sale. Eventually the sergeant laughed, and a truce was declared over a pot of tea.

Mr Traill explained Bobby's story and Sergeant Scott, as he'd introduced himself, was happy to blether about regimental pets. The latest pet dog at the Castle had died and the Sergeant knew Bobby would make an ideal replacement. The two men were shortly joined by a weel-kent burgh constable, who speired, 'I didna ken ye had a dog, John.' Mr Traill countered, 'So? Ye dinna ken everything, Davie!'

The next day, a rather peeved Davie, pit aboot by the landlord's retort, thrust a summons into Traill's hand. He was to answer the charge of owning a dog without a licence – an offence in those days. Traill made off to look for help from the Lord Provost, well known as an animal lover. The court case came with Traill fighting for Bobby's rights, but the case was mysteriously postponed. Then Ailie, now working at Traill's Dining-Rooms, was suddenly asked to have Bobby washed and brushed. Bobby was to attend an important meeting – with the Lord Provost, Mr William Chambers, no less!

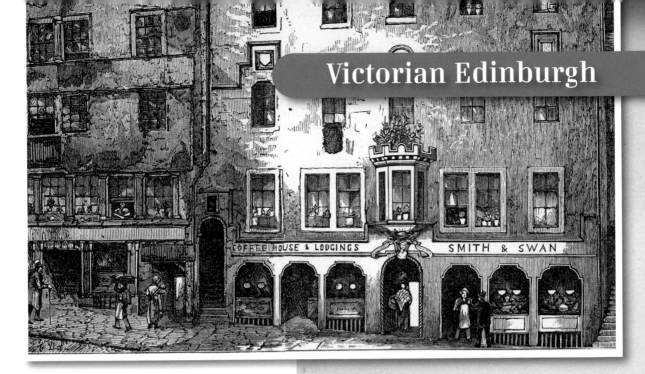

Scots corner

cantie	spirited
peeved	moody, ill-tempered
pit aboot	upset, put out
speired	asked, inquired
weel-kent	well known, familiar

Law and order

Edinburgh's Town Guard, of about 120 men, were mostly recruited from Highland Regiments. They used to patrol the streets and keep order during executions and state visits. Then, in 1805, an Edinburgh City Police was established to oversee the day- and night-watchmen. It had 30 wards, each with a General, two Commissioners and several watchmen.

Visit the Police Centre on the Royal Mile. It is not only a small museum, but still provides a working police service for any-one lost or reporting a crime.

Heave-awa Hoose

Only three years after Auld Jock died, in 1861, a whole seven-storey tenement collapsed in the High Street. Every floor gave way, leaving only the back wall in place. Twenty-five families lived in the building and many also had lodgers: 35 people were killed. One boy, half-buried under the rubble, called to the rescuers, 'Heave awa lads, I'm no deid yet!' He was pulled to safety. The rebuilt tenement at Paisley Close (near John Knox House) is today known as 'Heave-awa Hoose' and has a carving of the boy's head above the close entrance.

Two Edinburgh constables, c.1850 (right and far left).

Meeting the Lord Provost

All tricked out in his Sunday best, Mr Traill took time to inspect the freshly groomed Bobby.

Back in the Dining-Rooms, Ailie bumped into Sandy McGregor. Sandy knew all about the case, and explained to Ailie about the seven shillings needed for a dog licence. This was an enormous sum for someone brought up in a poor slum tenement. When Tam appeared later on, asking for Bobby, Ailie sobbed, 'Oh Tam, Mr Traill's gone to gie 'im up!'

The pair of them quickly worked out a plan of action for collecting the seven shillings from their neighbours in Candlemaker Row. It was a plan that had to be enacted at once. They worked from door to door, helped by other bairns – just like the Pied Piper. Soon they were only fourteen pennies short of their total. Geordie Ross, now a medical student, spared them a sixpence, and he persuaded a couple of his fellow students to do likewise.

Meanwhile, outside St Giles and unaware of the stushie at the Dining-Rooms, the Lord Provost was inspecting Bobby approvingly. Mr Chambers was nearly 70 years old, with a great sweep of white hair and full, square-cut white beard. He'd heard Traill explain Bobby's story at the court. Himself a country-man from Peebles, he knew many folk just like Auld Jock. Traill quietly pleaded with the canny provost not to let Bobby be parted from the Kirkyard, or banished to the Castle.

Suddenly Bobby's ears pricked up at the sound of Ailie's excited voice. She cried out, 'Bobby's no deid! Tam's got the money in his bunnet!' A great pile of coppers glinted as Ailie and Tam confronted the trio.

Humbled by the sight of these impoverished children, who only wanted to save their beloved Bobby, the Lord Provost asked them, 'Do ye ken aboot the freedom o' the city?' He quietly searched in his coat pocket and came out with a new leather collar, complete with shiny inscription: 'GREYFRIARS BOBBY, from the Lord Provost 1867 Licenced.'

The collar was passed from hand to hand in wonder and the bairns' eyes shone with pride. Bobby's future suddenly looked safe. The collar was buckled securely around his neck, by no less than the Lord Provost himself!

HIGH KIRK OF ST GILES

Victorian Edinburgh

- **Edinburgh City Chambers** is the head-quarters of Edinburgh District Council. First built as the **Royal Exchange** – a place for merchants and lawyers in the 18th century – it wasn't a huge success as they preferred doing business out in the street or in the coffee-houses. The building has four storeys in front on the High Street, and twelve storeys behind, facing down Cockburn Street.

- Underneath the City Chambers is a cobbled street, **Mary King's Close**, or 'the street that time forgot'. It has the remains of ancient houses and shops. Plague victims were bricked up there in the 1600s. The close is well worth a visit, but a tour is not for the faint-hearted!

- Opposite the City Chambers is the **High Kirk of St Giles**, where John Knox once preached. The church is dedicated to the patron saint of beggars and cripples. If you venture inside, look for the stained glass window dedicated to the poet Robert Burns.

  St Giles is often called a cathedral. Its correct name is the High Kirk of Edinburgh. It was only a cathedral during the years when it had a bishop (1633-38 and 1661-89). In 1637 an outraged member of the congregation, Jenny Geddes, threw her stool at the bishop: the new order of service was not to her liking!

- **Luckenbooths** (locked traders' booths) were built onto the outside of St Giles until around 1800. These included shoe-makers, snuff-makers, grocers, bakers, printers, watchmakers and jewellers. One luckenbooth had been the work-shop of George Heriot, goldsmith to King James VI (see page 19).

A soldier's world

Scots corner

haar	sea-mist
quirky	resourceful
wabbit	weary

Ranks of swinging kilts, red jackets and plumed bonnets marched down from the Castle in drill formation.

By now, Bobby had been returned to the Kirkyard by a grateful Mr Traill. The wee terrier wrestled with his stiff new collar, but skipped along as soon as he heard the military band. As the gate chinked open, wee Bobby was off, skeltering around the soldiers' legs. Their route march took them five long miles, up and down hill, and south by Fairmilehead, close to the farm that Bobby remembered well.

Nose to the ground, Bobby sought out the farm and trotted around the weel-kent sites of dairy, barns and hen-house. He barked in a friendly way to the young lady in the yard, who whirled around and cried, 'Oh Bobby! Have ye come hame?' With the kitchen door ajar, Bobby crept in under the corner settle where Auld Jock used to sit. An overjoyed Elsie didn't hear the bugle sound for the soldiers to reassemble. But Bobby heard it, and made to go just as the distraught Elsie found his new collar. 'He isna ma ain Bobby any more!' she sobbed, as Bobby scampered back to rejoin the troops.

The platoon marched back to the Borough-muir, east by Arthur's Seat and back up the Canongate to the Castle. Even Bobby was wabbit! Then the One o'Clock Gun stunned him with its explosion, and he dashed off to find refuge at the top of the Castle near the chapel. And who spied him? It was Sergeant Scott of the Royal Engineers, who had once tried to relieve Mr Traill of this feisty wee dog – and now fancied claiming him once again.

FIRING A CEREMONIAL GUN

Left: A Hill and Adamson photograph of soldiers of the Gordon Highlanders at Edinburgh Castle in 1846, watching as a ceremonial gun is fired.

Bobby was proudly introduced all around the Castle and finally left shut in the chapel. Now all that Sergeant Scott had to do was dine at Mr Traill's and negotiate for Bobby. But quirky Bobby knew the Castle would never be his home.

Down below the Castle a slow haar was rolling in from the sea, smothering the tombstones in the Greyfriars Kirkyard where the local bairns were desperately searching for their dog. Where was he? For the first time ever, the Kirkyard gate was left unlocked, so that Bobby could return safely to guard and to rest on Auld Jock's grave.

Website watch

Download your free guide to a children's trail around Edinburgh Castle and take it with you when you visit:

www.edinburghcastle.gov.uk/index/tour/quickguides.htm

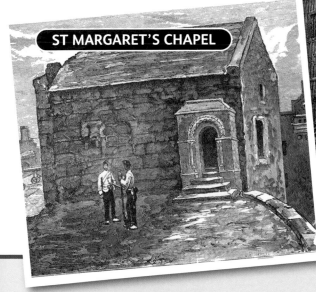

ST MARGARET'S CHAPEL

HALF-MOON BATTERY

Edinburgh Castle

- **St Margaret's Chapel** – This tiny chapel (above) sits at the highest point of the Castle Rock and is one of the oldest buildings in Edinburgh. It was probably built by King David I in the early twelfth century, in memory of his mother, the saintly Queen Margaret. For 300 years it was used as a gunpowder store, but interest shown by Queen Victoria in the tiny chapel resulted in its restoration after 1845.

- **The One o'Clock Gun** – The procedure for firing this gun was once overseen by a Colour-Sergeant Scott. It used to be fired from the curved **Half-Moon Battery**, but is today fired from the Argyle Battery.

Feted at the Castle

This Victoria Cross was awarded to Company Sergeant C. Coghlan, 75th Highlanders, for gallantry in Delhi, India, during the Mutiny that began in 1857.

The chapel door was slightly ajar as Bobby sneaked out from the shadows …

He was unusually baffled about an escape route. He had been lifted, teased and had romped with so many soldiers that – in desperation – he bit one on the hand. Now, avoiding all lights and voices, he tried to sniff a familiar way out – but the Castle was like a maze.

Finally, Bobby slipped into the old Governor's House, where officers were dining. A toast was being drunk to himself, no less! The Sergeant was apologising for Bobby's absence, explaining that he was still somewhere within the Castle. At the mention of his name, Bobby put his paws on an officer's knee. Suddenly he was placed on the table, beside all the glaizie regimental silverware.

42ND HIGHLANDERS

The Crimean War

Some of the soldiers at Edinburgh Castle in Bobby's time would have fought in the Crimean War (1853-56). Here are some facts about the war between Britain and Russia.

- **The Royal Scots Greys** were a cavalry regiment which took part in the war. You can find the statue to them in Princes Street Gardens. The regular army around 1860 had many famous Highland and Lowland Scottish regiments, including the regiment of the Crimean veterans in this photograph (right).

- **Victoria Cross medals** for bravery (above) are made from metal from a Russian cannon captured in the Crimea. They were first presented by Queen Victoria in 1857.

- Find out about **'The Charge of the Light Brigade'**, perhaps in the famous poem by Alfred Lord Tennyson.

Handled again and stroked, an officer felt Bobby's collar and read out the inscription. The whole table cheered the dog as he lay there, and then he let out his pleading yelp. 'Let him out at once, Sergeant, and stop this cruelty!' the officer commanded. Bobby soon gave the Sergeant the slip. Amid all the noise of booming foghorns from the Forth, the wee dog knew that the only way back to Greyfriars was downwards.

Claws splitting from scraping the Castle Rock, paws tender from the gorse bushes, Bobby scrambled, leapt, and rolled until he tumbled into a stableyard above the Grassmarket. Then he dragged himself up the causey-stanes of Candlemaker Row and pushed open the Kirkyard gate.

Army tales

- Wives often followed their soldier husbands into battle in the Crimean War. They were lodged in tents behind the British lines and washed clothes, darned socks, and tried to lessen the horrors of a Crimean winter.

- In the American Civil War, the famous 79th New York Highlanders was made up of Scottish soldiers. Wearing kilts and bonnets, they were led into battle by the bagpipes.

It was late morning before Ailie and Tam found the puggled wee dog. Their friend Geordie Ross, the medical student, proudly carried Bobby into the caretaker's house. Bathed and fed, the wee dog soaked up all the attention. He was back again where he belonged.

Above: *The Thin Red Line* by Robert Gibb was painted in 1881. It shows the 93rd Highlanders defending the port of Balaclava, 25 October 1854, during the Crimean War.

Scots corner

causey-stane	cobblestones
glaizie	glittering, shiny
puggled	exhausted

EDINBURGH CASTLE FROM ST GILES HIGH KIRK

Celebrity status

After many eventful years in his adopted home, Bobby became a celebrity.

This was partly because Greyfriars Kirkyard was the last resting place of many notable people – not least John Gray, Auld Jock himself. But now Bobby's fame had spread and visitors came from far and wide to see him. Bobby was spending less time chasing and hunting vermin, and taking more naps and dreaming of his early days in the Pentland Hills. But he still made his daily visit to Mr Traill's Dining-Rooms at the boom of the One o'Clock Gun.

One visitor to the Kirkyard was Baroness Burdett-Coutts, the 'Grand Leddy' (see page 32). Mr Traill had told her the story of Bobby. And the Baroness had listened to Tam and Ailie, who wondered if the wee dog would be remembered. As a champion of Bobby's life-long loyalty, the Baroness proposed that a suitable monument be designed, in bronze, to sit just outside the Kirkyard gate.

The 'Grand Leddy' was a great dog lover – just like Queen Victoria. She wanted a memorial with a low basin for water at a level that dogs could lap from. The upper section would have water too, with a cup, for thirsty people passing by. It was opened with great

Watering hole!

Drinking from a public water pump or fountain in 19th-century Edinburgh (see above picture) was a dangerous thing to do! Diseases such as cholera and typhoid, which could be caught by drinking contaminated water, were common.

fanfare – speeches, martial music and a prayer from the Minister of Greyfriars. Bobby was blissfully unaware of the fuss – his remarkable life was coming to a close. The little dog died one freezing January night in 1872. He was about sixteen.

Today you only have to visit Greyfriars and sit for a short time to notice the swarms of tourists from all around the world. Why do they all go quietly to Auld Jock's tomb and then study Bobby's own grave in the unconsecrated ground at the entrance to the Kirkyard? Who has passed on to them the story of this fiercely loyal Skye terrier? Perhaps it's a story with no frontiers – just one that everyone admires, loves and remembers.

Royal dogs

Did you know that **Mary, Queen of Scots** hid her pet Skye terrier when she went to her execution in 1587. After her death, it crept out from under her dress. The dog refused to eat and died of a broken heart.

Another queen, this time **Queen Victoria**, bred Skye terriers in the royal kennels. She had a favourite dog called **Islay**. The Duke of Argyll had gifted her two terriers and the royal connection made the breed very popular. From her early years, the Queen loved sketching dogs.

Victoria's son, later **King Edward VII**, set up an official Royal Kennels at his residence at Sandringham, specialising in the breed of Welsh Corgi which is favoured by Queen Elizabeth II today.

Animal memorials

- Learn about **Bamse**, a huge St Bernard's dog who was a Second World War hero in the Norwegian Navy. Where is his memorial? Find out at
  www.bamsemontrose.co.uk

- Go online to find out about Queen Victoria's dog **Islay** (see 'Royal dogs' below, left), and also about the talking dog statue! It stands outside the historic Queen Victoria Building in Sydney, Australia.

EDWARD VII AT A DOG SHOW

29

William Chambers

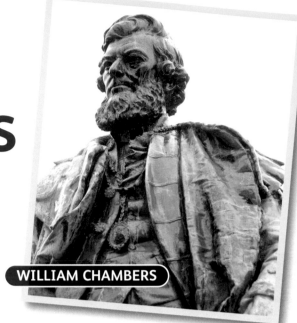

WILLIAM CHAMBERS

In this and the following pages there are three individuals who stood up for Bobby.

William Chambers (1800-83) was the Lord Provost of Edinburgh from 1865 until 1869, and led Edinburgh's Town Council. He was also a very successful businessman, having set up the publishing business of W. & R. Chambers in 1823, with his brother Robert, from a shop in Broughton Street.

The brothers pioneered cheap books and journals for the masses. So successful were they, that by 1832 Chambers's *Edinburgh Journal* was printing over 30,000 copies per week. They later produced textbooks and dictionaries, after having published the People's Editions of books by famous authors such as Tobias Smollett, Robert Burns, Walter Scott, Daniel Defoe, and many others. They were the popular paperbacks of their day.

The brothers also found time to write numerous 'improving' books, many of them very successful. One of William's titles was called *Fiddy: An Autobiography of a Dog* (1851), early evidence of his love of animals.

Chambers was a great Victorian improver. He was critical of the city's dreadful sanitary conditions in the 1840s; he helped to found the Pilrig Model Dwellings Company in 1849. Many of his other housing reforms and improvements were included in the City Improvement Act of 1867 – the same year Greyfriars Bobby received his smart collar inscribed with the Lord Provost's licence (see page 22).

Chambers was active in slum clearance across the Old Town, and in the restoration of public buildings and churches. He was also an early member of the Royal Society for the Prevention of Cruelty to Animals (RSPCA).

Chambers Street is named after the Lord Provost, with his fine statue half-way along, facing the steps of the National Museum of Scotland. On its base are representations of Literature, Liberality and Perseverance. Visible

300 metres to the west, on George IV Bridge and opposite the west end of Chambers Street, is the little statue of Greyfriars Bobby (see page 28). So the wee dog (in bronze) remains within sight of his benefactor (also in bronze, see opposite page).

Below: The Royal Scottish Museum in Chambers Street, as it was in the early 20th century. William Chambers's statue (opposite page and in the picture below) was erected in 1891 outside the museum.

Chambers Street

Construction of the Industrial Museum of Scotland in Chambers Street began in 1861 and became the Edinburgh Museum of Science and Art. It was designed by Francis Fowke and was inspired by the Crystal Palace of the Great Exhibition of 1851 (see page 2), first opening to the public in the early 1890s. Renamed the Royal Scottish Museum in 1904, the museum has undergone many renovations and extensions, and it is now known as the National Museum of Scotland.

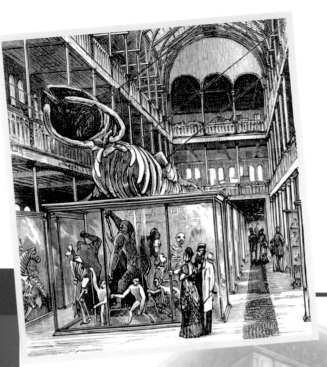

Above: A gallery in the Edinburgh Museum of Science and Art.

Angela Burdett-Coutts

Another of Bobby's champions, Baroness Angela Burdett-Coutts (1814-1906), was said to be the richest heiress in Britain at the time of our story.

During the Crimean War, the Baroness (above) sent the nurse Florence Nightingale a linen drier, which she had designed herself, for hospital laundry. Find out more about the ground-breaking work of Florence Nightingale during the Crimean War and afterwards.

Known as the 'Grand Leddy', the Baroness was five years older than Queen Victoria. Her Scots grandfather, Thomas Coutts, founded the London bank that still bears his surname, and was a Member of Parliament. Life-long friends included the Duke of Wellington (to whom she proposed marriage), and Prime Ministers Gladstone and Disraeli. Lots of men wanted to marry her for her wealth, and suitors were numerous.

Burdett-Coutts was made a baroness by the queen for her generosity. Known as 'the Queen of the Poor', she was a good friend of Victoria, even helping her financially in the early years of her reign. She eventually married at 66, in 1881.

Burdett-Coutts knew Scotland well and was a frequent visitor at Balmoral Castle. She met Bobby in 1871, when she commissioned his bronze statue from sculptor William Brodie. She knew Chambers through his work with the Royal Society for the Prevention of Cruelty to Animals, and received the freedom of the city of Edinburgh in 1874, not long after Greyfriars Bobby's statue was unveiled.

She spoke at RSPCA meetings all over the country, believing that 'life, whether in man or beast, is sacred' – and all forms of cruelty to animals were detestable to her. In 1873 she drew attention to the ill treatment of Edinburgh's tram-horses.

Baroness Burdett-Coutts's wealth was vast. She was a generous benefactor of the church, RSPCA, ragged schools for homeless children, homes for destitute women – the list was endless. Her good friend, the author Charles Dickens, gave her much sage advice, and she was a campaigner for many good causes.

William Brodie

Artist William Brodie (1815-81) created the Greyfriars Bobby statue in 1871.

He is said to have created the life-size bronze from the life. The work was commissioned by Baroness Burdett-Coutts, who gifted the little statue to Edinburgh Town Council.

By the 1870s Brodie was one of Edinburgh's most successful sculptors. He had already made several of the statues that adorn the Scott Monument on Princes Street, representing characters from Sir Walter Scott's 'Waverley' novels. A smaller replica version of the statue of Amy Robsart (a tragic figure in Scott's novel *Kenilworth*, 1821) was gifted to Lord Provost Chambers, and now sits in the Chambers Institute in Peebles.

Another famous Brodie statue is the seated, pensive figure in Princes Street Gardens of Sir James Young Simpson (1877), pioneer anaesthetist and doctor of obstetrics; he was the Queen's doctor in Scotland. With his younger brother Alexander, Brodie had also created a fine marble bust of Queen Victoria in 1865/66.

William Brodie's successful reputation saw him elected in 1851 to membership of the Royal Scottish Academy, a fine Greek classical building in Princes Street. The RSA was Edinburgh's – and Scotland's – foremost learned society for artists and sculptors. Other illustrious learned societies were the Royal College of Surgeons at Surgeons' Hall on the South Bridge, the Royal Society of Edinburgh in George Street, and the Faculty of Advocates that occupied the old Scottish Parliament Building beside St Giles.

These organisations were not exactly clubs, but in Victorian times their members were very proud to be elected to them; it usually meant that they had arrived at the top of the tree in their chosen field.

The **Royal Scottish Academy** at the foot of The Mound, Princes Street, Edinburgh. In this picture it is partly obscured by the **Scott Monument**.

Edinburgh's epidemics

Edinburgh suffered a smallpox outbreak between 1740 and 1742, followed by typhoid fever and cholera outbreaks in 1831-32 and 1838-40.

Citizens were at last getting worried about the squalor of their Old Town; but only after the 1861 collapse of a whole tenement in the High Street did the Town Council act (see page 21).

In 1862 the city appointed its first public health officer – Dr Henry Littlejohn. He reported that Edinburgh's high death rate from disease was due to the appalling living conditions in the Old Town – not least the habit of throwing all waste into the street.

(see page 21).

Dr Henry Duncan Littlejohn

Dr Henry Duncan Littlejohn (1826-1914) was the first medical officer of health in Scotland. He had been a police surgeon and lectured in forensic medicine at Edinburgh University. His vision helped to make the city a better place to live in. He was deeply involved with William Chambers in the building of Victorian Edinburgh and in the provision of a municipal fever hospital – the City Hospital – which opened in 1903 at Greenbank.

The cry of 'Gardy-loo!' respected no one – pauper or peer. Littlejohn recommended paving and draining closes; limiting the number of people in each tenement; introducing water and gas; cleaning common stairs; and opening up the worst of the narrow alleys. All these ideas were fully supported by Lord Provost William Chambers.

The Royal Infirmary

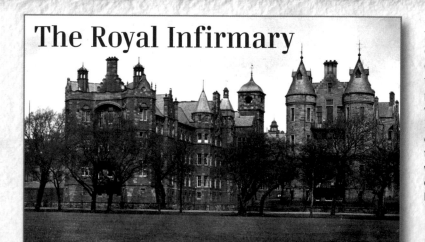

The original infirmary, pictured on page 9 (in Infirmary Street, off the Cowgate), 'a hospital for the destitute sick', was the last place Auld Jock wanted to visit when he was ill. The new Royal Infirmary, by the Meadows, opened in 1879 and was soon training doctors from all over the world. (It moved to its current green-field site in Edinburgh's Little France area in 2003.)

REVD DR THOMAS GUTHRIE

Stockbridge signs

If you walk around the Stockbridge colonies in the north-west of Edinburgh, you will see the plaques at the ends of terraces showing the trades of some of the first house-owners – such as a plasterer, joiner, mason, slater or draughtsman. Many of these artisans' colonies in Stockbridge were developed by the Co-operative Society, which uses a beehive for its company logo. The Labour Movement also adopted this image in the mid-1800s. Do you know why?

Answer on page 40

Leading churchmen by the mid-1800s also felt the need to act. Dr Thomas Guthrie (1803-73) was concerned about the homeless and neglected children who roamed the streets. He founded schools where they were fed, taught the 'three Rs', and learned a trade. These were the 'Edinburgh Original Ragged Industrial Schools', or Dr Guthrie's Schools. The first opened in 1847 in Ramsay Lane, below the Castle Esplanade.

While wealthier Edinburgh professionals had moved to the spacious New Town, tradesmen welcomed the initiatives of the Edinburgh Co-operative Building Society, founded by another minister, James Begg (1808-83). This company built the city's first 'colonies', a series of neat terraced houses, each with its small garden. The earliest were at Stockbridge (1861-75), Hawthornbank (1863-64), Ferry Road (1865-67), Dalry (1867-70) and Maryfield (1867-77). Begg's vision is set out in his publication *Happy Homes for Working Men: and how to get them* (1866).

The **Edinburgh United Industrial School** was an example of a 'ragged school', which was supported by voluntary contributions. Its aim was to 'relieve, educate and reclaim the neglected and outcast children of the city'.

Bobby's Edinburgh

DOG CEMETERY

Here are some of the key places in Edinburgh associated with Greyfriars Bobby.

You can take a 3D tour and fly in and around a virtual Edinburgh Castle at:

www.edinburghcastle.gov.uk/ index/tour

The **Castle Rock** at **Edinburgh Castle** is the remains of an extinct volcano, shaped by the last Ice Age. The steep crags of the volcanic core made attack extremely difficult.

The **dog cemetery** (above) is a small garden within the Castle. It has been in use since the 1840s as a burial place for officers' pet dogs and for regimental mascots. It can only be viewed from the ramparts above it. (There is said to be the ghost of a dog wandering the garden.) There is a similar dog cemetery at Fort George, near Inverness.

The **One o'Clock Gun** is fired every day except Sunday and is now kept solely as a visitor attraction. There is no cannonball nowadays – the signal is a 'time gun' and the noise was heard as far away as ships on the Forth, allowing them to set their time-piece to the exact time. In 1861 an electric cable linked the Castle's clock to a large time-ball at the top of the Nelson Monument on Calton Hill. When the cannonball was fired at the Castle, the time-ball simultaneously dropped at the top of the Monument, and this movement could be observed from tele-scopes on ships far away. (In its day, this Victorian innovation was the longest electric cable in the world at 1237 metres long!)

NELSON MONUMENT

FLODDEN WALL

Bobby's friends Geordie Ross and Sandy McGregor both attended **George Heriot's Hospital**, then a charity school. The school's eastern gate still leads directly into Greyfriars Kirkyard.

Steeped in history, **Greyfriars Kirkyard** is the burial ground of many famous Edinburgh citizens, including James Craig (designer of the New Town), Joseph Black (chemist and physicist), George Buchanan (tutor to James VI), and many others. Most visitors today head straight for Bobby's grave at the entrance, and then inspect Auld Jock's headstone. Originally outwith the old City Wall, there is still a section of the **Flodden Wall** within the Kirkyard.

GEORGE HERIOT'S SCHOOL

GREYFRIARS BOBBY
DIED 14TH JANUARY 1872
AGED 16 YEARS

LET HIS LOYALTY & DEVOTION
BE A LESSON TO US ALL

The **Cowgate** was a narrow canyon-like street which housed the poor and destitute of the Old Town. It became an even darker place after the building of George IV Bridge across it in the early 1830s.

At the head of the cobbled **Candlemaker Row** once stood the Hall of the ancient Corporation of Candlemakers. From 1500 until the early 1800s candle-making was an important craft; it only died away after the introduction of gas lighting.

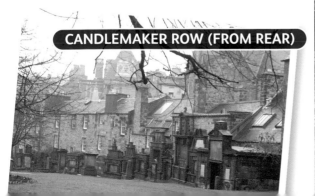

CANDLEMAKER ROW (FROM REAR)

THE COWGATE

37

Bobby's breed: why the name?

Skye terriers take their name from the Isle of Skye. They are the oldest terrier breed in Scotland, going back to the 14th century.

They were needed to get rid of vermin. Terriers were bred for hunting ability, both on land (for catching foxes, badgers and rabbits) and on water (for destroying otters).

Skye terriers stand about 25cm high and twice as long as they are high. Their thick coat falls straight to the ground, and they have larger ears than those of their cousin, the Cairn terrier. Colours range from black, blue-black, grey, silver, fawn or cream. They are excellent watchdogs, and very loyal to their owner. They are sensitive and active dogs, and – like Bobby – they don't like to be teased.

Website watch
RSPCA

To find the story behind the **RSPCA**, the best known animal welfare organisation in the world, go to:

www.rspca-education.org.uk

Find out about the famous White House pets in the United States of America. They go back as far as George Washington. Most of the US Presidents kept dogs, but some also had more unusual pets – you can find out what they were at:

www.presidentialpetmuseum.com

Guide dogs for the blind

Modern guide dogs started in Germany in 1916-17 when dogs were trained to lead soldiers blinded by poisonous gas in the First World War. Today's Guide Dogs for the Blind Association is the world's largest breeder and trainer of dogs. Guide dogs have transformed the lives of many people by giving them dignity and independence. The Association also invests millions of pounds in research into eye disease.

Puppies start training at around one year old (or seven in dog years). Training lasts about five months, when they are ready for their new owner. They work for about seven years and then get a well earned retirement. Most guide dogs are Labrador retrievers, but other breeds are also used – such as Alsatians, boxers and Border collies.

Man's best friend

Around the City of Edinburgh, in the middle of busy streets and leafy parks, statues to the great and good have been raised over the centuries. Look closely, and there, beside the poet, artist, scientist or town worthy, is often a loyal companion. Here are some notable examples!

A statue of a dog called **Bum**, from San Diego, USA, one of Edinburgh's twin cities, was unveiled in Princes Street Gardens in 2008. Bum's story was similar to Bobby's and he lived among San Diego's 'bums', or vagrants and boozers, in the late 19th century.

SCOTT AND MAIDA

The famous Scott Monument, dedicated to **Sir Walter Scott**, features a statue of the writer with his favourite dog, a deerhound called **Maida**.

HOGG AND HECTOR

There are other statues around Scotland of famous people who share their monuments with their animals. This statue of James Hogg, known as the 'Ettrick Shepherd', is at St Mary's Loch in the Ettrick Valley. Hogg was a popular writer from the Scottish Borders who favoured plain shepherd's clothes and preferred to write much of his work in Scots. His sheepdog is called **Hector**.

MAXWELL AND TOBY

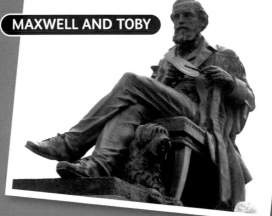

James Clerk Maxwell was interested in the Science of Physics, especially in light sources and photography. His statue is on George Street, just before St Andrew Square. His loyal companion was a dog called **Toby**.

39

ANSWERS

Page 7: **Windy Door Nick** – this name comes from the Gaelic *Gaothach Dorus nan Eag*, which means 'windy door in the notch, or gap'.

Page 11: **Water for sale** – the pipes are made from hollowed-out sections of tree wood.

Page 12: **Mystery object** – This mort-collar from Fife, dated *c.*1825, held down a newly-buried corpse in its grave, so that 'Resurrectionists' (body-snatchers) could not steal it for anatomical dissection.

Page 13: **The Martyrs' Monument** – A martyr is a person killed for their cause, usually their religion. The Covenanters demanded freedom to worship according to the forms of the presbyterian Church of Scotland. Many of the Covenanters' leaders were beheaded; some were drowned. The Martyrs' Monument says of the hundred or so leaders, 'the most part of them lie here' (i.e. minus their heads).

Page 19: **Mystery object** – This is the Heriot Loving Cup thought to have been owned by George Heriot. Its maker was Robert Denneistoun in 1611-13. The 'cup' is made out of a nautilus shell, a very unusual and exotic object for this time.

Page 35: **Stockbridge signs** – The bee is known for its industry and is hard-working. It is also a good co-operator within the organisation of the hive.

ANSWERS – Facts and activities –

Page iv: **Puzzle page: 'City link!' word search** – The 20 words related to the places and people of Edinburgh in Bobby's time are highlighted in the box below. The answers to the **Criss-crossword** are as follows: (1) Jinglin Geordie; (2) Greyfriars; (3) rats; (4) Cowgate; (5) wabbit; (6) Swanston; (7) Rab; (8) licence; (9) hot mutton broth; (10) Skye terrier

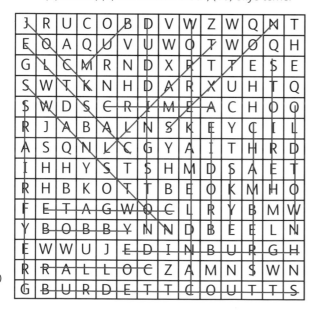

ANSWERS
Facts and activities section –

Page v: **Celebrity dogs** –
(1) = B (Nipper); (2) = E (Luath); (3) = F (Toto); (4) = A (Nana); (5) = C (Pongo); (6) = D (Maida)

USEFUL WEBSITES

BBC – for information on Victorian Britain
www.bbc.co.uk/history/forkids

Edinburgh – for a 'tour' of the city
www.walktalktour.com

Greyfriars Bobby – for information on the story
www.Greyfriarsbobby.co.uk
www.historic-uk.com/HistoryUK/
Scotland-History

Historic Scotland – for information on Edinburgh Castle
www.edinburghcastle.gov.uk

National Galleries of Scotland – for information on the Scottish National Photography Collection within the Scottish National Portrait Gallery
www.nationalgalleries.org

National Museums Scotland – see 'National Museum of Scotland' for information on Scotland during the 19th century in 'Industry and Empire'
www.nms.ac.uk

RSPCA – for information on the work of the RSPCA and interactive resources
www.rspca-education.org.uk

SSPCA – for information on the work of the Scottish Society for the Prevention of Cruelty to Animals
www.scottishspca.org

Wikipedia
www.wikipedia.org

PUBLICATIONS

Greyfriars Bobby, by Eleanor Atkinson (Puffin Classics, Penguin Books Ltd, 1994 edition).

The Tale of Greyfriars Bobby, by Lavinia Derwent (Puffin Books, 1985).

Greyfriars Bobby

Facts and activities

This book belongs to:

_____

Write your name on the above line.

PLACES OF INTEREST

Listed below are a number of places associated with Greyfriars Bobby in and around the City of Edinburgh. There are guided walks to get you around the City's High Street or Royal Mile, especially during the summer months, and Tourist Information offices can also assist you:

Museum of Edinburgh, 142 Canongate (0131 529 4143)

Museum of Childhood, 38 High Street (0131 529 4142)

National Museums Scotland (0131 225 7534) including the **National Museum of Scotland**, Chambers Street **National War Museum of Scotland** at Edinburgh Castle **Museum of Scottish Country Life** East Kilbride

Edinburgh Castle including the **Scottish National War Memorial, St Margaret's Chapel** and the **Argyle Battery** – Historic Scotland (0131 225 9846)

Outlook Tower and **Camera Obscura**, Castle Hill (0131 226 3709)

Edinburgh Police Centre, 188 High Street (0131 226 6966)

Greyfriars Kirk and Kirkyard, Candlemaker Row (0131 226 5429)

High Kirk of St Giles, High Street (0131 225 9442)

Nelson Monument, Calton Hill (0131 556 2716)

George Heriot's School, Lauriston Place. Access limited during term time.

Swanston Village and T-wood, approximately 1 mile walk from Oxgangs Road, near Fairmilehead

---

FURTHER CREDITS

BRITAIN'S KING AND QUEEN: THE STORY OF THEIR LIVES by Thomas Paul (John F. Shaw & Co.: London, 1901) – for page 29 (King Edward VII at dog show)

CASSELL'S *OLD AND NEW EDINBURGH: Its History, its People, and its Places* by James Grant (Cassell & Co: London, n.d.) – for pages 9 (Grassmarket); 10 (Edinburgh tenements); 11 (Canonball House); 14 (Robert Burns); 21 (Heave-awa Hoose); 22 (William Chambers); 23 (St Giles Kirk); 25 (St Margaret's Chapel & Half-Moon Battery); 33 (Scott Monument & Royal Scottish Academy); 35 (Thomas Guthrie, beehive & United Industrial School); 37 (Cowgate)

CITY ART CENTRE, EDINBURGH – for page 7 ('View of Edinburgh from the vicinity of Craiglockhart', attributed to Revd John Thomson of Duddingston, 1778-1840)

THE COMPREHENSIVE HISTORY OF ENGLAND: Civil, Military, Religious, Intellectual and Social – Macfarlane and Thomson (Blackie & Son: Glasgow, n.d.) – for pages 2 (Great Exhibition); 3 (Russian soldiers); 29 (Mary, Queen of Scots & Queen Victoria)

EDINBURGH CITY LIBRARY (courtesy of Edinburgh City Libraries and Information Services – Edinburgh Room) – for page 11 (image of water caddie from James Colston: *Edinburgh and District Water Supply* – TD262[G80734])

EDINBURGH LIFE 100 YEARS AGO – 'from Captain Topham's Letters' (William Brown: Edinburgh, 1886) – for page 20 (Town Guard)

EDINBURGH UNIVERSITY LIBRARY (Lothian Health Services Archive) – for page 9 (first Royal Infirmary)

GEORGE HERIOT TRUST (The Governors of George Heriot's Trust) – for pages 18 (school emblem); 19 (copy of a portrait of George Heriot, attributed to John Scougall, 1615 & for the Loving Cup)

GETTY IMAGES® (www.gettyimages) – for page 32 (Angela Burdett-Coutts)

GREYFRIARS KIRK (photograph – by kind permission of the The Society of the Friends of the Kirk of the Greyfriars) – for page 13 ('Greyfriars Bobby' by John McLeod)

FRANCES and GORDON JARVIE (©) – for page 37 (Flodden Wall)

LIFE JOTTINGS OF AN OLD EDINBURGH CITIZEN – Sir J. H. A. Macdonald KCB (T. N. Foulis: Edinburgh, 1914/15) – for pages 20 (day-policeman); 21 (night-policeman)

MEMORIALS OF EDINBURGH IN THE OLDEN TIME – Daniel Wilson FRSSA (Hugh Paton: Edinburgh, 1843) – for pages 11 (Cowgate); 12 and cover (Greyfriars Kirk)

NATIONAL ARCHIVES OF SCOTLAND (SCOTLANDSIMAGES.COM/Crown Copyright 2007 The National Archives of Scotland)) – for page 36 (East End of Princes Street, Edinburgh)

NATIONAL LIBRARY OF SCOTLAND (Reproduced by kind permission of The Trustees of the National Library of Scotland) – for page 15 (Robert Louis Stevenson)

THE NEW STUDENT'S REFERENCE WORK – Chandler B. Beach and Frank Morton McMurry (F. E Compton & Company: Chicago, 1914) – for Eleanor Atkinson image.

ROYAL COMMISSION ON THE ANCIENT AND HISTORICAL MONUMENTS OF SCOTLAND (Crown Copyright 2007) – for page 27 (Edinburgh Castle from St Giles Kirk)

SCOTTISH NATIONAL PHOTOGRAPHY COLLECTION, SCOTTISH NATIONAL PORTRAIT GALLERY – for page 18 ('Greyfriars Bobby', photograph, c.1865, artist unknown [detail])

JOHN DOUGLAS WILSON (©) – for pages 8 (Candlemaker Row); 13 (Martyrs' Monument); 36 (Dog Cemetery); 37 (Bobby's gravestone & Candlemaker Row); 39 (Bum, Sir Walter Scott statue & Sir James Clerk Maxwell statue); Facts and activities section, page v (Maida and Luath on statues)